COUNT DRACULA
AND THE VICTIM

Count Dracula sat in his coffin
and had a sulk.
"I'm fed up. It's not fair."

1

Frankenstein's Monster came to
find the Count.
"Hello Count."

"Get out, I want to be on my own."
"All right," said F.M. "Then I'll go and answer the door."

"No," shouted Dracula.
"This is **my** castle and **I** open the door.
Ha! This time it may be a victim."

"I hope so," said F.M.
"A victim would be fun."

Count Dracula opened the door.
F.M. and the ghost watched from
the top of the stairs.

"Come in, come in," said the Count.
"Welcome to my castle."

In came a young man.

"A victim at last," whispered the Count.

"Can I spend the night in your castle?"
asked the man.

"Please do, you are very welcome,"
said the Count.

9

The Count and the young man
had supper together.
F.M. served them.

"I didn't scare him, not one bit,"
said F.M.
"I'll scare him, just you watch,"
said the ghost.

After supper the Count took
the young man upstairs.
The ghost tried to scare him.
He just smiled.

"Something is not right,"
moaned the Count.
"But I shall bite him anyway."

The young man went to bed
Dracula went to get ready.

Dracula went to bite him.
The young man sat up.

"I'm not a victim," he said.
"I'm a werewolf.
I've come to live in your castle too."